MW00770078

GALATIANS
AND
ROMANS

Galatians section by Catherine Upchurch

Romans section by Clifford M. Yeary

Little Rock
Scripture Study

*A ministry of the Diocese of Little Rock
in partnership with Liturgical Press*

Dear Friends in Christ,

Sacred Scripture is a wealth of inspired wisdom expressing Christian truths which challenge us to deepen our relationship with God. Although the Bible can be intimidating, it is important that we study God's word in the Scriptures, because it is the basis of our faith and offers us the thoughts and experiences of Christians past and present. It is God speaking to us through the insights of Church fathers and later saints.

I am pleased to present this study guide from Little Rock Scripture Study to serve as an aid for reflection and contemplation in your reading of Scripture. At the same time, the guide will give you insight into how to apply what you have read to your life today.

I encourage you to read Sacred Scripture slowly and reflectively so that it can penetrate your heart and mind. It is my hope that the Word of God will empower you as Christians to live a life worthy of your call as a child of God and a member of the body of Christ.

Sincerely in Christ,

✠ Anthony B. Taylor
Bishop of Little Rock

Sacred Scripture

"The Church has always venerated the divine Scriptures just as she venerates the body of the Lord, since from the table of both the word of God and of the body of Christ she unceasingly receives and offers to the faithful the bread of life, especially in the sacred liturgy. She has always regarded the Scriptures together with sacred tradition as the supreme rule of faith, and will ever do so. For, inspired by God and committed once and for all to writing, they impart the word of God Himself without change, and make the voice of the Holy Spirit resound in the words of the prophets and apostles. Therefore, like the Christian religion itself, all the preaching of the Church must be nourished and ruled by sacred Scripture. For in the sacred books, the Father who is in heaven meets His children with great love and speaks with them; and the force and power in the word of God is so great that it remains the support and energy of the Church, the strength of faith for her sons, the food of the soul, the pure and perennial source of spiritual life."

Vatican II, Dogmatic Constitution on Divine Revelation, no. 21.

INTERPRETATION OF SACRED SCRIPTURE

"Since God speaks in sacred Scripture through men in human fashion, the interpreter of sacred Scripture, in order to see clearly what God wanted to communicate to us, should carefully investigate what meaning the sacred writers really intended, and what God wanted to manifest by means of their words.

"Those who search out the intention of the sacred writers must, among other things, have regard for 'literary forms.' For truth is proposed and expressed in a variety of ways, depending on whether a text is history of one kind or another, or whether its form is that of prophecy, poetry, or some other type of speech. The interpreter must investigate what meaning the sacred writer intended to express and actually expressed in particular circumstances as he used contemporary literary forms in accordance with the situation of his own time and culture.

For the correct understanding of what the sacred author wanted to assert, due attention must be paid to the customary and characteristic styles of perceiving, speaking, and narrating which prevailed at the time of the sacred writer, and to the customs men normally followed in that period in their everyday dealings with one another."
Vatican II, Dogmatic Constitution on Divine Revelation, no. 12.

Instructions

MATERIALS FOR THE STUDY

This Study Guide: Galatians and Romans

Bible: The New American Bible with Revised New Testament or The New Jerusalem Bible is recommended. Paraphrased editions are discouraged as they offer little if any help when facing difficult textual questions. Choose a Bible you feel free to write in or underline.

Commentary: *Galatians and Romans* by Brendan Byrne, S.J. (Liturgical Press) is used with this study. The assigned pages are found at the beginning of each lesson.

ADDITIONAL MATERIALS

Bible Dictionary: *The Dictionary of the Bible* by John L. McKenzie (Simon & Schuster) is highly recommended as a reference.

Notebook: A notebook may be used for lecture notes and your personal reflections.

WEEKLY LESSONS

Lesson 1—Galatians 1
Lesson 2—Galatians 2:1–3:14
Lesson 3—Galatians 3:15–4:31
Lesson 4—Galatians 5:1–6:18

Lesson 5—Romans 1:1-17
Lesson 6—Romans 1:18–3:20
Lesson 7—Romans 3:21–4:25
Lesson 8—Romans 5:1–6:23
Lesson 9—Romans 7:1–8:13
Lesson 10—Romans 8:14–9:5
Lesson 11—Romans 9:6–11:36
Lesson 12—Romans 12:1–14:23
Lesson 13—Romans 15:1–16:27

YOUR DAILY PERSONAL STUDY

The first step is prayer. Open your heart and mind to God. Reading Scripture is an opportunity to listen to God who loves you. Pray that the same Holy Spirit who guided the formation of Scripture will inspire you to correctly understand what you read and empower you to make what you read a part of your life.

The next step is commitment. Daily spiritual food is as necessary as food for the body. This study is divided into daily units. Schedule a regular time and place for your study, as free from distractions as possible. Allow about twenty minutes a day. Make it a daily appointment with God.

As you begin each lesson read the indicated pages of the commentary and the appropriate Scripture passages where indicated. This preparation will give you an overview of the entire lesson and help you to appreciate the context of individual passages.

As you reflect on Scripture, ask yourself these four questions:

1. *What does the Scripture passage say?*
   Read the passage slowly and reflectively. Use your imagination to picture the scene or enter into it.

2. *What does the Scripture passage mean?*
   Read the footnotes and the commentary to help you understand what the sacred writers intended and what God wanted to communicate by means of their words.

3. *What does the Scripture passage mean to me?*
   Meditate on the passage. God's Word is living and powerful. What is God saying to you today? How does the Scripture passage apply to your life today?

4. *What am I going to do about it?*
   Try to discover how God may be challenging you in this passage. An encounter with God contains a challenge to know God's will and follow it more closely in daily life.

THE QUESTIONS ASSIGNED FOR EACH DAY

Read the questions and references for each day. The questions are designed to help you listen to God's Word and to prepare you for the weekly small-group discussion.

Some of the questions can be answered briefly and objectively by referring to the Bible references and the commentary *(What does the passage say?)*. Some will lead you to a better understanding of how the Scriptures apply to the Church, sacraments, and society *(What does the passage mean?)*. Some questions will invite you to consider how God's Word challenges or supports you in your relationships with God and others *(What does the passage mean to me?)*. Finally, the questions will lead you to examine your actions in light of Scripture *(What am I going to do about it?)*.

Write your responses in this study guide or in a notebook to help you clarify and organize your thoughts and feelings.

THE WEEKLY SMALL-GROUP MEETING

The weekly small-group sharing is the heart of the Little Rock Scripture Study Program. Participants gather in small groups to share the results of praying, reading, and reflecting on Scripture and on the assigned questions. The goal of the discussion is for group members to be strengthened and nourished individually and as a community through sharing how God's Word speaks to them and affects their daily lives. The daily study questions will guide the discussion; it is not necessary to discuss all the questions.

All members share the responsibility of creating an atmosphere of loving support and trust in the group by respecting the opinions and experiences of others, and by affirming and encouraging one another. The simple shared prayer that begins and ends each small-group meeting also helps create the open and trusting environment in which group members can share their faith deeply and grow in the study of God's Word.

A distinctive feature of this program is its emphasis on and trust in God's presence working in and through each member. Sharing responses to God's presence in the Word and in others can bring about remarkable growth and transformation.

THE WRAP-UP LECTURE

The lecture is designed to develop and clarify the themes of each lesson. It is not intended to be the focus of the group's discussion. For this reason, the lecture always occurs *after* the small-group discussion. If several small groups meet at one time, the groups may gather in a central location to listen to the lecture.

Lectures may be presented by a local speaker. They are also available on CD and DVD.

Galatians I

GALATIANS AND ROMANS, PAGES I–14

Day I

1. What do you already know about Paul that draws you to study his Letter to the Galatians?

2. Given that we cannot be certain of the location of Paul's audience, what can we know about their identity and the general reason Paul was writing to them? (See introduction in the commentary; Gal 1:6-7; 4:13-20.)

3. Why does the author of your commentary believe that it is unfair to look for anti-Judaism or anti-Semitism in Paul's Letter to the Galatians?

Day 2

(Note: The commentary gives a fine summary of the entire book of Galatians with good signposts about what to find along the way. We will examine the book closely as we go along and proceed now directly into the biblical text.)

4. From whom did Paul receive the authority to call himself an apostle (1:1)? (See Acts 9:1-9, 15.) Pg 2016

5. What conditions for apostleship might some early Christians have insisted on? (See Acts 1:21-26.)

6. In Paul's greeting to the Galatians, what aspect of Jesus' mission is highlighted and why (1:4)?

Day 3

7. Who originated the call of the Galatians that Paul refers to in 1:6? (See 5:7-8.)

8. When Paul refers to the "grace of Christ" what does he mean (1:6)? (See Rom 3:24; 11:5-6; Eph 1:7; 1 Tim 1:14-15; commentary glossary.)

9 Identify at least one way you have experienced or witnessed what Paul means by grace.

Intellgent

ey expected him to be a political leader

. Holocaust

Jesus, Christ

Faith

God

Faith in Jesus

Day 4

10. Paul's curse of those who "pervert the gospel of Christ" (1:7-9) demonstrates the seriousness of his concern and his commitment. What was the meaning of such a curse in this period of history?

11. What does Paul mean by calling himself a "slave of Christ" (1:10)? (See Rom 1:1; 1 Cor 7:22-23.)

12. Recall some of the details of Paul's "former way of life in Judaism" (1:13-14). (See Acts 8:1-3; 22:3-5; 26:9-11; 1 Cor 15:9; Phil 3:5-6.)

Day 5

13. In this brief account of his conversion, Paul simply says "God, who from my mother's womb had set me apart and called me through his grace, was pleased to reveal his Son to me" (1:15-16a). What more information is available? (See Acts 9:1-19; 22:6-21; 26:12-18.)

14. When you look back over your life, how has the Son of God been revealed to you?

15. In speaking of the time after his encounter with Christ, why does Paul emphasize how little contact he had with the other apostles in Jerusalem (1:12, 15-19)?

Day 6

16. What can you learn about the other Christian leaders mentioned in 1:18-24? (See Matt 14:28-31; 16:15-19; Mark 1:16-18; 3:16-17; Acts 15:6-20.)

17. Paul reveals that the churches in Judea only knew him by reputation, for bad and for good (1:22-24). How would his conversion story have helped to pave the way for them to accept him?

Galatians 2:1–3:14

GALATIANS AND ROMANS, PAGES 14–26

Day 1

1. Are there any insights from last week's sharing or lecture that you would like to discuss before moving on?

2. Why was Paul concerned about seeking consensus regarding Gentile converts (2:1-2)? (See Acts 9:15; 14:26–15:2.) *2026*
   2153   *2017 2026*

3. How were the "false brothers" trying to "enslave" the converts to Christianity (2:4)? (See 3:1-3.) *4*
   2153   *2154*

Day 2

4. What seems to be the purpose of Titus accompanying Paul on this journey to Jerusalem (2:3-5)?

5. Identify some of the differences in the two accounts of what we call the Council of Jerusalem (2:1-10; Acts 15:1-21).

6. What could account for the differences between Paul's account of the meeting in Jerusalem (2:1-10) and Luke's account found in Acts 15:1-21?

Day 3

7. Identify some of the phrases in Galatians 2:1-10 that demonstrate Paul was not pursuing human approval for his divinely given mission.

8. What was the specific meaning of being "mindful of the poor" (2:10), and why was Paul eager to respond? (See Acts 11:27-30; Rom 15:25-28.)

9. Why was Paul later critical of Peter and Barnabas for withdrawing from sharing a meal with Gentile converts in Antioch (2:11-14)? Was Paul justified in his criticism?

Day 4

10. What does Paul mean when he says "we, who are Jews by nature and not sinners from among the Gentiles" (2:15)? (See Rom 3:9.)

11. When Paul speaks of "justification" (2:16-21), what does he mean? (See 3:11; Rom 3:19-26; commentary glossary.)

12. In this section of Galatians, how does Paul describe sin (2:17-18)?

Day 5

13. In Galatians 2:18-21, Paul speaks very personally about his life in Christ. If you were to list some of the things that you have left behind so that you can live in Christ, what would you include?

14. Spend a few moments praying with the phrase "Christ lives in me" (2:20). Are there any times in your life that you became particularly aware of this truth?

15. Paul speaks about beginning with the Spirit and ending with the flesh (3:3).

    a) In this passage how is he using the term "flesh"?

    b) What does he mean by "the Spirit"? (See 5:4-5; Rom 5:5.)

Day 6

16. How was Paul able to turn around the appeal to Abraham as the ancestral father of God's people (3:6-9)? (See Gen 12:3; 15:1-5; 18:18; Jas 2:23.)

17. Why are those dependent on the "works of the law" said to be under a curse (3:10)? And what does Paul say is the remedy for such a curse (3:13)?

18. What is the background for the language of "ransom" that Paul uses when referring to Christ (3:13)?

Galatians 3:15–4:31

GALATIANS AND ROMANS, PAGES 26–38

Day 1

1. What new insights about the law did you gain from the previous lesson?

2. According to Paul's argument, why doesn't God's covenant with us depend on the law given through Moses (3:17-18)? (See Rom 4:16.) 2070   2154

3. Are the law and God's promise in opposition with one another (3:21)? (See Rom 7:7.) 2073
   2155

Day 2

4. In what sense does Paul mean that the law acts as a "disciplinarian" (3:24-25)? 2155

5. Recall a baptism that you witnessed in the recent past. In what ways do we symbolize being "baptized into Christ" and being "clothed with Christ" (3:27)? 2155

6. Unity in Christ Jesus is emphasized in Paul's words, "neither Jew nor Greek . . . neither slave nor free person . . . not male and female" (3:28). (See 1 Cor 12:13; Col 3:11.) Where do you see in your own faith community that superficial divisions are being overcome? And where do you see the need for greater unity?

Day 3 2155 2138

7. How does Paul demonstrate that all who believe in Christ are heirs to the promise of God (4:1-5)? 2155

8. What is the significance of being able to call God "Abba" (4:5-7)? 21⁵
   (See Mark 14:36; Luke 11:2; Rom 8:15-16.) 2074
   1870   1908

9. At this point in the letter, Paul speaks of coming to know God
2155 and God knowing us (4:9). Have you experienced a deep sense of knowing and being known by God? How would you describe that? (See Pss 25:4-5; 100:3; 139:1-24.)

985 99 1080

Day 4

10. Paul admonishes believers not to be lured into old habits and beliefs (4:9-10). What are some of the temptations and false thinking that might lure believers today to abandon true faith? (See Phil 3:18-20; Col 2:20-22.) 2188
2179

11. What is Paul referring to when he says "I have also become as you are" (4:12)? 2155

12. Have you ever experienced a situation where speaking the truth endangered a previously good relationship (4:13-16)? 2155

Day 5

13. What is the nature of Paul's criticism of others who are showing interest in the Galatians (4:17-19)?

14. Identify Hagar and Sarah (scan Gen 16–21). What do we know about them?

15. Sarah is usually associated with Judaism and Hagar with those outside of Judaism. How and why does Paul reverse these expectations (4:21-31)?

Day 6

16. What was the original context for understanding the numerous children of a barren wife? How does Paul use that same passage in his Letter to the Galatians (4:27)? (See Isa 54:1.)

17. Is Paul really calling for the expulsion of the Jews (4:30)? Or is he trying to demonstrate the dangers of legalism?

18. Has your experience of being a Christian been more about freedom or more about being obedient? How do you reconcile these two?

Galatians 5:1–6:18

GALATIANS AND ROMANS, PAGES 38–51

Day 1

1. Recall something gained from the previous session that deepened your understanding of Paul's theology.

2. Paul speaks to the Galatians of being freed from the "yoke of slavery" (5:1). To what is he referring, and what other kinds of slavery might we be freed of in Christ? (See John 8:36; Eph 2:1.) 2/65

2156   1967

3. What religious practices might we be guilty of overemphasizing and thus call into question the benefits freely given by Christ
2156 (5:2)? (See 2:21.) 2154

Day 2

4. What difference does it make in your understanding to realize that Paul's criticism of the law is directed primarily to Gentile believers and not to Jews (5:2-4)? 2156

5. If circumcision was unnecessary and bound a man to every aspect
2156 of the law (5:3), what are the circumstances that earlier caused Paul to insist that his assistant, Timothy, be circumcised? (See Acts 16:1-3.) 2028

6. Provide some local examples of "faith working through love"
215 6(5:6). How could these actions impact those who witness or receive them? (See Jas 2:12-13; 1 Pet 2:16-17.) 2277

Day 3   2258

7. a) What are some common misunderstandings about freedom?

   b) How does Paul intend freedom to be understood (5:13-14)? (See Rom 13:8-10.) 2081   2157

8. Can you describe a call to serve others that you found difficult but also expanded your ability to give and receive love (5:13)? 2157

9. After seeming to berate obedience to the law, why does Paul now praise fulfilling the whole law (5:14)? 2157

Day 4

10. Review and summarize the meaning that Paul wants to convey when he speaks about the tensions between "flesh" and "the Spirit" (5:16-17). (See Rom 7:22-23; 8:5-6; Eph 2:3-5.)

11. a) When reviewing the works of the flesh (5:19-21), why do you suppose some of the vices listed there get more attention than others?

    b) When reviewing the fruit of the Spirit (5:22-23), what lessons do you learn about the value of community life?

12. What are some ways to deal with tension in each of us between the flesh and the Spirit (5:17-26)? (See Eph 5:15-17; 6:18.)

Day 5

13. What can you learn from this passage (6:1) and from other passages in the New Testament about correcting others? (See Matt 7:1-5; 18:15-18; John 8:3-11.)

14. Recall a time when others in your faith community helped you to bear a burden (6:2). What was being communicated to you through their care? (See Col 3:12-14.)

15. Consider what you have sown in the past year or two. What do you expect to reap (6:7-9)? Would this make a good examination of conscience?

Day 6

16. What was happening politically in Israel that may have added to the felt pressure to insist on circumcision (6:12-13)?

17. Paul boasts in the cross of Jesus Christ and says he "bear[s] the marks of Jesus" on his body (6:14-17). What "marks" do you carry in your person that testify that you belong to Christ? (See 1 Cor 2:2; 2 Cor 4:8-11.)

18. In our religious tradition, how does one become a "new creation" (6:15), and what are the signs you notice in your own life that you are a new creation?

2158

Autonomery
6.13
Liviodicus
18 & 19

LESSON 5

Romans 1:1-17

GALATIANS AND ROMANS, PAGES 53–68

Day 1

1. What do you recall concerning Paul's purpose in writing the Galatians?

2. What are some of the reasons the commentary suggests Paul's Letter to the Romans is so different in tone from Galatians?

3. What subject does Paul tackle in Romans that makes this letter "the most influential document in Christian theology"? (See commentary.)

Day 2

4. What are three characteristics of ancient letters that are also found in Paul's Letter to the Romans (1:1-15)? (See commentary.)

2066

5. Many have noted that letter writing is a dying art in modern times. What do you think we stand to gain or lose by relying on modern communication technology?

6. What are the two ways of identifying Jesus that Paul emphasizes in 1:3-4?

Day 3

2066

7. In what ways does Paul's description of who Jesus is (1:3-4) go beyond what the commentary calls "conventional Jewish messianic expectation"?

8. What special gift does Paul say Jesus Christ has given him, and to what purpose has he been given this (1:5-7)? 2066

9. Paul understood the Gospel to be the good news of salvation for all the peoples of the world. From your own ethnic heritage, what people(s) do you represent as having accepted this good news (1:5-6)?

2. He has not himself founded the community.
The tone is more formal even hesitant.

Day 4

10. In what ways does your faith community recognize the diversity of peoples who have been called to faith in Christ?

11. Read the Shema prayer (Deut 6:4-9). What are the three things this prayer calls faithful Jews to do?

12. Who are the people in your life whose faithfulness and witness to goodness give you reason for offering thanks to God (1:8-10)?

Day 5

13. Paul has never been to Rome, but he is very thankful for their faith, which has been "heralded" everywhere (1:8). When have you been made aware of Christians whose faith has received (or ought to be given) wide publicity for worthy reasons?

14. Why might Paul have felt it necessary to explain that he had not yet visited Rome (1:13)?

15. When Paul writes of the "Greeks," to whom is he actually referring (1:14)?

Day 6

16. Paul is eager to preach the Gospel (1:15) to the same Romans whose faith he says is heralded throughout the world.

    a) With what frequency do you hear the core message of the good news of Jesus Christ proclaimed in your own faith community?

    b) In what ways have you been called to give witness to the gospel in your own faith community, in your family, and in the world at large?

17. What are the two key areas that the author says God (in the Old Testament) required righteousness from people (1:17; see commentary)?

18. Romans 1:16-17 is said to state the actual theme of Romans. Can you restate that theme in your own words?

11. The Lord is our God. Love him c̄ your whole heart, being + strength.

12

13

17.

Romans 1:18–3:20

GALATIANS AND ROMANS, PAGES 68–80

Day 1

1. From the previous lesson, what is something you recall about either the Christians in Rome or Paul's reasons for writing them?

2. The commentary suggests that Romans 1:18-31 is "in many ways the most forbidding and least attractive part of Romans." What were your personal feelings and impressions as you read this section?

   What was the "wrath" of God as written about in the Old Testament (1:18)? (See Exod 15:7; 22:21-23; Deut 11:16-17; Isa 51:22-23; Jer 50:6-13; Hos 14:3-5; Nah 1:2.)

Day 2

4. What is Paul's purpose in describing the pervasiveness of sin in the world and its ultimate consequences (1:18-31)? 2066 + 67

5. What does Paul say can be known about God through awareness of the created world (1:19-20)? (See Acts 17:22-28.) 2030

6. What do you find in the created world (or universe) that helps 2066
   you appreciate some characteristic of the Creator?

Day 3

7. a) What does Paul suggest is the proper response of humans who recognize that the created world points to an "invisible" Creator (1:21)? (See 1 Thess 5:18; Rev 4:8-9.)

   b) What sin did humans commit instead of giving the proper response (1:21-22)?

8. Idol worship does not seem to be prevalent today, but what else besides God do modern people become tempted to worship? (See Col 3:5.)

9. What differences exist between Paul's understanding of human sexuality and what we know today (1:24-28)? (See commentary; 1 Cor 6:9b-10; 1 Tim 1:9-10.)

Day 4

10. Beginning at 2:1, Paul addresses his thoughts to an unnamed "you." Who might this person be and why might Paul be doing this? (See commentary.)

11. a) Why does Paul warn against making judgments of others (2:1-3)?

    b) What differences are there between Paul's warning against judging others and Jesus' similar teaching (Matt 7:1; Luke 6:37)?

12. What argument does Paul make to prove that circumcision actually makes no real difference in one's relationship with God (2:25-29). (See Gal 5:2-6; Col 3:11.)

Day 5

13. What are "the utterances of God" that Paul says God entrusted with the Jewish people (3:2)? ▾

14. How has studying "the utterances of God" changed, challenged, or rewarded the way you seek or understand the presence of God in your life?

15. What part of Paul's message was apparently misconstrued by some to mean "we should do evil that good may come of it" (3:1-8)? (See 5:8, 20; 6:1; 11:32.)

Day 6

16. Why is it such an important part of Paul's gospel to claim that everyone, Jew and Gentile alike, is sinful (3:9)? (See Gal 3:22; 1 Cor 1:30.)

17. If the Mosaic law wasn't given to help make people righteous, what does Paul say was its purpose (3:20)?

18. What does the commentary suggest is the positive light we should see shining on this section of Romans (1:18–3:20)?

The whole Old Test.

Romans 3:21–4:25

GALATIANS AND ROMANS, PAGES 80–93

Day 1

1. Look at how you answered question number 2 in last week's lesson. If your impressions or feelings concerning Romans 1:18–3:20 changed since studying it, how have they? *2066*

2. Put in your own words the definition of righteousness found in the glossary of the commentary. (See 3:21-22.) *2069*

3. It would seem that learning that everyone, Jew and Gentile alike, "have sinned and are deprived of the glory of God" (3:23) would be bad news. How does Paul preface this to assure us that this is actually good news (3:21-22)? *2069*

Day 2

4. What is the dual nature of God's righteousness that Paul mentions in 3:21-22? *2069*

5. How have both aspects of this dual righteousness been manifested in Christ (3:21-26)?

6. Why is it so important for Paul to explain Abraham's role in salvation history (4:1-25)? (See Gen 15.) *P9 49*

   2069-70

. Those who believe

Day 3

7. Jesus' parable about the workers in the vineyard is one that often perplexes modern hearers and readers (Matt 20:1-16). How might Paul's comments on wages in 4:5 provide a possible perspective for understanding the parable?

8. Paul quotes a psalm attributed to King David to express the joy of being declared righteous in spite of being a sinner (4:7; Ps 32:1-2). Why would David have particular reason to express this kind of happiness? (See 2 Sam 11:2-17; 12:7-13.)

9. The commentary describes being declared righteous as a restoration of good relationship with God, similar in concept to reconciliation (pp. 81–83). When have you experienced the joy that springs from being reconciled with someone?

Day 4

10. a) Read Genesis 15:1-8. What are the two promises God makes to Abraham (Abram)?

    b) Why is it so important to Paul that God made these promises to Abraham before he was circumcised (4:16)?

11. What matters have you entrusted with God out of belief in God's faithfulness?

12. According to Paul, why was the rite of circumcision given to Abraham (4:11)?

1 adoration contrection Thanksgiving
petition

Day 5

13. God promised Abraham that his descendents would inherit a specific land (Gen 15:18-21). Why does Paul say the promise was to "inherit the world" (4:13)? (See Gen 1:27-28; commentary.)

14. How did Abraham's call to become a faithful follower of God begin (Gen 11:24–12:4)?

15. Paul calls Abraham the father of both the circumcised (4:1, 12) and the uncircumcised (4:6-12, 16-17). What importance might it be to Christians to be able to claim Abraham as our father?

Day 6

16. What makes Abraham's faith in God so similar to a Christian's belief in the resurrection of Christ (4:17-19)?

17. How has Paul's explanation of Abraham's justification by faith (4:1-25) also been a demonstration that, rather than "annulling the law," he is "supporting the law" (3:31)?

18. Few Christians today are concerned about whether circumcision is a religious necessity or not. What value do you think Paul's explanation of Abraham's faith might still have for modern Christians?

14 Through Righteousness.

12.1

Romans 5:1–6:23

GALATIANS AND ROMANS, PAGES 93–106

Day 1

1. What is something you recall from last week's study concerning Abraham and his importance to Christian faith (4:1-25)?

2. In what ways has the gift of faith made you conscious of God's presence in your life, your family, and the world around you?

3. Is belief in justification by faith (5:1) something that is only part of Protestant faith, or is it a Catholic doctrine as well? 2071

Day 2

2071

4. What does it mean to you to have "peace with God" (5:1)? (See Eph 2:14.) 2165

2071

5. What is it that Jesus Christ has given us access to (5:1-2)? (See Eph 2:13-18; Heb 4:13-16; 10:19-22.) 2241
2165   2235

6. What is this "glory of God" which Paul says we can boast in our hope of attaining (5:1-2)? (See Gen 1:26-27; 2 Cor 3:9-18; 1 John 19563:2; commentary.) 2071   35   2129

Day 3

7. a) What sort of affliction(s) have you ever had to endure (5:3-5)?

   b) What dangers and/or advantages do you see in Paul's assessment of the value of enduring afflictions (5:3-5)? (See 1 Cor 12:9-10; Jas 1:2-4; 1 Pet 1:5-7.)

8. Paul is certain the Roman Christians are aware that God's love for us has been "poured out into our hearts through the holy Spirit" (5:5). How has this awareness made a difference in your own spiritual life?

9. a) According to Paul, how has God proved his love for us (5:6-8)? (John 3:16; 1 John 4:10.)

   b) How have you experienced sacrificial acts of love from others in your life?

2. More peace in our life as we bring our concerns to God.

+ Surrender to God.

Day 4

10. What point is Paul trying to make by contrasting Adam's sin with Jesus' righteous act (5:12-21)? (See 1 Cor 15:20-22, 45-49.)

11. Paul says that death is a result of sin (5:12). (See 6:23.) In what ways can you see the link between sin and death?

12. What does Paul say makes it unthinkable that Christians might continue in sinful lifestyles after they have come to believe in Christ (6:1-14)?

Day 5

13. a) Recall a baptism you have attended, or perhaps even your own. Among the symbols and prayers and rituals employed in baptism what stands out in your memory?

    b) How is our dying and rising with Christ in baptism (6:3) emphasized in the Catholic Church's rite of baptism?

14. Which baptismal imagery, that from Galatians (3:27) or Romans (6:3), do you find more inspiring, and why so?

15. In what sense does Paul regard our bodies as "weapons" (6:12-14)? (See 13:12; Eph 6:11-17.)

Day 6

16. Slavery was very common in Roman society. How would you explain what Paul is saying about our duty to become slaves of Christ without using the image of slavery (6:15-23)? (See 12:1.)

17. Who are the ones, in your life and experience, who have best demonstrated what Paul means by "slavery" to Christ?

18. Paul addresses the Romans as Christians who have experienced a conscious conversion to faith in Christ (6:17). In what ways have you consciously chosen to have faith in Christ?

Romans 7:1–8:13

GALATIANS AND ROMANS, PAGES 106–120

Day 1

1. What is something important to you that you gained from last week's lesson?

2. How is our release from the law like a woman who has become a widow (7:1-6)? (See Eph 2:13-15; 5:25-33.) 2168
   2073   2165
3. What does Paul teach elsewhere concerning widows and remarriage within the Christian community? (See 1 Cor 7:8-9.)

Day 2

4. What example does Paul give to support his claim that the law actually produces sinful passions (7:5-7)? (See Exod 20:17; Deut 5:21; Matt 5:27-28.) 365 /771/   148

5. In Romans, Paul teaches that death comes as a result of sin (5:12-14). What kind of death does Paul associate with sin and the law in 7:9-10?

6. If the law actually increases sinful passions, which in turn have a deadly effect on us, why would Paul still affirm that the law is holy, righteous, and good (7:11-13). (See 1 Tim 1:8-9.)

Day 3

7. What is Paul's objective in detailing the law's failure to deliver us from sin (7:1-25)?

8. a) What experiences have you had of an environment where simply having rules failed to prevent wrongdoing or misbehavior?

   b) In your experience, what is needed beyond knowing right from wrong to promote positive behavior?

9. Paul says, "I do not do what I want, but I do what I hate" (7:15). What reason does the commentary give for suggesting he wasn't really speaking about his own experience in much of 7:14-25? (See Phil 3:4-6.)

Day 4

10. What big switch in the tone and atmosphere of Romans occurs in 8:1?

11. In a further contrast with Mosaic law, what does Paul say that Jesus' death and resurrection bring about in relation to the "righteous decree of the law" (8:1-4)?

12. The commentary says that the way Paul states Romans 8:4 has great ecumenical value for both Protestants and Catholics. What is this value?

Day 5

13. When have you witnessed a "righteous" (or "just") act that seemed spiritually inspired (8:4)?

14. Even though the doctrine of the Trinity would not be fully developed until centuries after Paul, what is the "trinitarian shape" the commentary finds in Romans 8:2-4?

15. What does Paul mean by living "according to the flesh" (8:5)? (1 Cor 3:2-3; Gal 5:16-17, 24; 6:7-8; Eph 2:3.)

Day 6

16. Paul says the spirit is concerned with life and peace (8:6). How does he expound on his list of spiritual things elsewhere? (Gal 5:22-23; Phil 4:8.)

17. What things in life make you most aware of the influence of the Holy Spirit?

18. What is the great hope of Christians that Paul turns his attention to in 8:10-13?

Romans 8:14–9:5

GALATIANS AND ROMANS, PAGES 120–133

Day 1

1. What is something you remember about Paul's understanding of the purpose of the Mosaic law, or how he contrasts grace and faith with the law?

2. The commentary says Romans 8 "is everyone's favorite" (p. 116). What were your feelings and impressions as you read this chapter and what drew the strongest response from you?

3. In your own spirituality, what is the significance to you that the New Testament emphasizes our relationship to God as that of a child to a parent (8:14)? (See Luke 11:2; Gal 3:26; 4:6; Phil 2:14-16; Heb 2:10; 1 John 3:1-2.)   2155

Day 2   1956

4. Recall Romans 6:16-23. How does Romans 8:15 affect the way a reader might understand that earlier passage?

5. Paul wrote to the Romans in Greek. What might be significant about Paul's use of the Aramaic word "Abba" for "Father," as well as the Greek "Pater" (8:15)? (See Matt 6:1-18; 10:20; 23:9; Mark 14:36; Gal 4:6; see commentary pp. 120–121.)
1870
6. As children of God, to what have we been made heirs (8:16)? (See Matt 25:34; Eph 1:13-21; Col 1:9-12; Heb 9:15; 1 Pet 1:3-5.)

Closed confession
started 800 by
Irish Monks.

48

Day 3

7. What place do you think suffering has within a healthy spirituality (8:17)? (See Acts 5:40-41; 9:15-16; 1 Cor 12:13-27; 2 Cor 1:5-7; Phil 3:7-11; Col 1:24; Heb 5:8-9; 1 Pet 1:6-7; 2:20-21; 3:14a; 4:1-2, 13.)

8. In what ways do you see that creation has been forced to share in the "corruption" of human beings (8:18-23)? (See Gen 3:17.)

9. Some Christians are very concerned about "the end of the world." What do Paul's words concerning creation being set free from its slavery to corruption suggest about God's ultimate purpose for creation (8:19-23)? (See Isa 66:22; 2 Pet 3:10-13; Rev 21:1.)

Day 4

10. How does Christian hope differ from simply wanting something to be true or real (8:24-25)? (See 5:1-5; 12:12; 1 Cor 13:13; Eph 1:18-23; 1 Thess 2:19; 4:13; 5:8; 1 Tim 4:10; Heb 6:17-18; 10:23; 1 Pet 1:3-5; 1 John 3:2-3.)

11. When, if ever, have you experienced a time where your groans might have been a prayer uttered through you by the Holy Spirit (8:26-27)? (See Exod 2:23-24; Ps 12:6; 38:10; 42:6; 77:4; 79:11; 2 Cor 5:2-4.)

12. How does the promise that everything will work for our good in Christ differ from a promise that nothing bad will ever happen to us (8:28)?

9. Renewal

10 Trust in God.

Day 5

13. We sometimes learn valuable lessons for life from unpleasant circumstances. Have you any experience of something that was not good in itself at the time working to the good for you later in life (8:28)?

14. The commentary claims that the "predestination" Paul speaks of in 8:29-30 is entirely positive. How is it suggested we are to understand Paul's statement that "Those he foreknew he also predestined to be conformed to the image of his Son"?

15. What unassailable evidence does Paul offer the Romans to prove that there is no power in heaven or on earth that can interfere with God's intention to save us (8:31-39)?

Day 6

16. Why might Paul's message that nothing can "separate us from the love of God in Christ Jesus our Lord" (8:39) so quickly turn to Paul's anguish over his people Israel (9:1-5)?

17. When has personal anguish over friends or family deepened personal bonds with them (9:1-3)?

18. Among the gifts that Paul says belong to Israel, which still belong to the Jewish people today (9:4-5)? (See 11:29.)

17 Periods of tradgy.

1.19.'23

Romans 9:6–11:36

GALATIANS AND ROMANS, PAGES 133–148

Day I

1. What stands out most for you from your study of Romans 8 last week?

2. What point is Paul trying to make about the differences in God's relationships with Isaac and Ishmael and also with Jacob and Esau (9:6-13)? 2076

   2072

3. What is the story of Jacob and Esau (6:13)? (See Gen 25:21-34; 27:1-46; Mal 1:3; Heb 12:15-17.)   63

Day 2 65   1740   2244

4. a) In demonstrating from Scripture that God's favor is a gift and not something that is earned (9:1-33), is there anything in Paul's argument that disturbs you? 2075

   b) How does the commentary try to resolve some of the discomfort Paul's argument might cause readers to feel?

5. In what way does Paul use the image of potter and clay to make his point (9:19-24)? (See Sir 33:11-13; Isa 45:9; Jer 18:1-10.) 1449

   2076

6. What is "the most terrifying doctrine ever to be drawn from Scripture," that the commentary says was taken from 9:20-22 in isolation from the rest of Scripture? (See Ezek 18:31; 1 Tim 4:10.)

   1558   2209

5. We are the potter in' God's hand who Can destroy us from evil.

Day 3

7. Paul quotes Hosea to affirm that God, in Christ, has made a people out of diverse Jewish and Gentile ethnicities (9:23-26). (See Hos 2:1, 25.) In what significant ways does your faith community celebrate this sense of being the people of God regardless of ethnic diversity?

1647

1649

8. Paul is concerned that many of his fellow Jews are trying to achieve righteousness through their own works (9:32). How could this also be a warning to us as Christians?

2077

9. What was the stone that made Israel stumble (9:32-33)? (See Matt 21:42; Luke 20:13-27; Acts 4:8-11; 1 Pet 2:1-8.)

2008   *2276*

Day 4

10. How can zeal for religion (any religion, including Christianity) that lacks discernment lead one away from God (10:2)? *2077*

11. What are at least two ways in which Christ can be understood as "the end of the law" in the New Testament (10:4)? (See Matt 5:17; Eph 2:14-16.)

12. How do Paul's quotations of Mosaic law in 10:5-13 illustrate the differences between two paths to righteousness? (See Lev 18:5; Deut 30:11-14.)

Day 5

13. Paul describes the confession of Christ as Lord as a simple act of faith, a "word" in effect, that saves us (10:9). In what circumstances could such a simple confession be a difficult and dangerous thing? (See 8:36; Matt 24:9; Mark 10:30; Luke 21:12-13.)

1862

14. a) Why is preaching the Gospel so essential to Paul's understanding of justification by faith (10:14-17)?

    b) St. Francis of Assisi said, "Preach the gospel everywhere. When necessary, use words." What is the most effective way you know of that the Gospel is preached in your civic community?

15. a) How does Paul respond to the notion that God has rejected Israel (11:1-5)?   *2078*

    b) Why does Paul see the conversion of Gentiles as a sign of hope for the Jews (11:11-14)?

Day 6   *2078*

16. In what ways can you see that the Jewish "roots" of Christianity continue to nourish the church (11:17-24)? (See 15:4; Matt 13:52; Mark 14:12-24; John 15:5.)   *1784*

17. What is Paul's certainty regarding Israel and its relationship to God (11:25-27)?

18. What is it that Paul finds so very positive in the fact that all peoples of the world are disobedient to God (11:32)?   *2079*

1.26.'23

Romans 12:1–14:23

GALATIANS AND ROMANS, PAGES 148–162

Day 1

1. What can you recall from the previous lesson in Romans (9:6–11:36) that either disturbed or inspired you?

2. How does the "spiritual worship" (12:1) Paul urges the Romans to engage in both build upon and transform the worship he says was God's gift to Israel (9:4)? (See 6:13; Deut 12:13-14.) *325*

3. a) What are some of the dangers that might result from conforming ourselves to the "age" in which we live (12:2)? (See Eph 4:22-24.) *2167*

   b) How can Christians engage in the transformation that Paul calls "the renewal of your mind" (12:2)? (See Phil 4:8.)

Day 2 *2080*

4. a) What gift or gifts has the Spirit given you for the good of the body of Christ (12:3-8)? (See 1 Cor 12:4-11; 1 Pet 4:10-11.) *2080*

   b) What gifts do you see in others near you?

5. How might your local parish or faith community go about recognizing and strengthening the gifts that each member has for the building up of the body of Christ (12:3-8)?

6. What does it mean to "anticipate one another in showing honor" (12:10) in our time and culture?

2080

Day 3

7. What "needs of the holy ones" are you aware of in your local community (also nationally and globally) that are in need of contributions (12:13)? (See 15:25-27; 1 Cor 16:1-3.)

8. When have you answered the call to literally "rejoice with those who rejoice" and "weep with those who weep" (12:15)?

9. Paul has written earlier in Romans concerning "the wrath" (1:18; 2:5-8; 3:5; 4:15; 5:9; 9:22). What does he mean in 12:19 by urging the "beloved" to "leave room for the wrath"? (See Lev 19:18; Deut 32:39-42.)   *Let God do it*   216

Day 4   354

2080

10. Some of Paul's admonitions in this section (12:9-21) tell us to respond to evil with goodness out of love simply because that is the right thing to do, but others seem to suggest that our charitable response to evil might still be an expectation of the evil-doer's ultimate punishment. What do you think Paul's ultimate position is? (See Matt 5:38-48.)

11. What is it about 13:1-7 that sets it apart from the rest of Romans or even any of Paul's other letters? *U must comply to civil authority*

12. What are the circumstances, if any, in which you think a Christian might have a moral obligation to refuse obedience to civil authority (13:1-7)? (See Acts 4:13-19.)

2008

Day 5

13. How does Paul's teaching on the fulfillment of the command-
    ments (13:8-10) compare with Jesus' teaching on the same? (See
    Lev 19:18; Matt 22:36-40; Mark 12:28-33; Luke 10:25-28; Gal 5:14.)

14. What does Paul offer as a motivation for selfless love of our neigh-
    bor (13:11)?

15. Who are the weak and strong in faith to whom Paul refers (14:1-
    6)? (See 1 Cor 8:4-13; Rev 2:14, 20.)

Day 6

16. What warning does Paul give to the "strong" in faith in regard to
    their behavior concerning the "weak" in faith (14:13-23)? (See 1
    Cor 8:7-13.)

17. What experience have you had of the kingdom of God, based on
    Paul's description of it in 14:17?

18. What wider application might Paul's teaching concerning con-
    science and the eating of foods sacrificed to idols have in modern
    life (14:20-23)?

LESSON 13

Romans 15:1–16:27

GALATIANS AND ROMANS, PAGES 162–173

Day 1

1. What is something you recall from the previous lesson concerning our relationship to one another as Christians?

2. Recall an example of neighborliness from your own life, in which someone went out of their way to help someone in need (15:1-2). (See Lev 19:18; Prov 27:10; Luke 10:30-37.) *1907*

3. How has reading and studying the Bible instructed you, encouraged you, or given you hope (15:4)? (See 4:23-24; 1 Macc 12:8-9; 1 Cor 10:11; 2 Tim 3:16; Heb 4:12.) *2105*   *2235*

Day 2

4. Does Paul's exhortation to think in harmony with one another and to praise God with one voice mean everyone must agree on everything (15:5-6)? (See 14:1-6.)

5. In what ways, if any, would you like to see your worshiping community become a more welcoming community (15:7)? (See Acts 6:1-4; Jas 2:1-5.) *2258* *2011*

6. What does Paul mean by saying that Christ became a minister of the circumcised (15:7)? (See Matt 15:24; Gal 4:4-5.)

Day 3   *2082*

7. In 15:13 Paul offers a prayer for the Romans' joy, peace, and hope. Who might you pray this prayer for today?

8. What does Paul say is his priestly service of the Gospel (15:15-16)? (See 12:1; 1 Pet 2:4-5.) *2267*

9. a) What has kept Paul from visiting the Romans (15:18-22)? (See 1:1-5; 11:13; 1 Tim 2:7.)

   b) Why is Paul planning to visit Rome now (15:23-29)? (See 1:11-12.)   *2083*   *2066*

Day 4

10. a) Why does Paul want to go to Jerusalem before going to Rome (15:25-28)? (See also 1 Cor 16:3-4; Gal 2:1-10.)

    b) How do we know Paul is apprehensive about going to Jerusalem (15:30-32)? (See Acts 20:22-23; 21:10-11.)

11. Who is Phoebe, what is her role in Cenchreae, and what is her relationship to Paul (16:1-2)? *She was a deacon minister.*

12. What do we know about Prisca (also called Priscilla) and Aquila from Romans and other New Testament sources (16:3-5)? (See Acts 18:1-3, 18, 24-26; 1 Cor 16:19; 2 Tim 4:19.)

Day 5

13. What does Romans 16:5 tell us about how the church was organized at the time? (See NAB footnote for 16:5; 1 Cor 16:19; Col 4:15; Phlm 1:2.)

14. Who are Andronicus and Junia (16:7)?

15. In what way has the greeting with a holy kiss been made part of our eucharistic liturgies (16:16)?

Day 6

16. What does it mean to you "to be wise as to what is good, and simple as to what is evil" (16:19)? (See Matt 10:16; 1 Cor 14:20.)

17. What is "the mystery kept secret for long ages" mentioned in 16:25? (See Eph 3:3-6, 9; Col 1:26-27; 2:2.)

18. As you conclude your study of Galatians and Romans, what do you think are the most enduring contributions these letters of the apostle Paul have made to Christian faith?

    Justification by Faith.

ABBREVIATIONS

Books of the Bible

Gen—Genesis
Exod—Exodus
Lev—Leviticus
Num—Numbers
Deut—Deuteronomy
Josh—Joshua
Judg—Judges
Ruth—Ruth
1 Sam—1 Samuel
2 Sam—2 Samuel
1 Kgs—1 Kings
2 Kgs—2 Kings
1 Chr—1 Chronicles
2 Chr—2 Chronicles
Ezra—Ezra
Neh—Nehemiah
Tob—Tobit
Jdt—Judith
Esth—Esther
1 Macc—1 Maccabees
2 Macc—2 Maccabees
Job—Job
Ps(s)—Psalm(s)
Prov—Proverbs
Eccl—Ecclesiastes
Song—Song of Songs
Wis—Wisdom
Sir—Sirach
Isa—Isaiah
Jer—Jeremiah
Lam—Lamentations
Bar—Baruch
Ezek—Ezekiel
Dan—Daniel
Hos—Hosea
Joel—Joel
Amos—Amos

Obad—Obadiah
Jonah—Jonah
Mic—Micah
Nah—Nahum
Hab—Habakkuk
Zeph—Zephaniah
Hag—Haggai
Zech—Zechariah
Mal—Malachi
Matt—Matthew
Mark—Mark
Luke—Luke
John—John
Acts—Acts
Rom—Romans
1 Cor—1 Corinthians
2 Cor—2 Corinthians
Gal—Galatians
Eph—Ephesians
Phil—Philippians
Col—Colossians
1 Thess—1 Thessalonians
2 Thess—2 Thessalonians
1 Tim—1 Timothy
2 Tim—2 Timothy
Titus—Titus
Phlm—Philemon
Heb—Hebrews
Jas—James
1 Pet—1 Peter
2 Pet—2 Peter
1 John—1 John
2 John—2 John
3 John—3 John
Jude—Jude
Rev—Revelation